Horn
Prep Test

ABRSM

Horn Prep Test

Dear horn player,

Welcome to your Prep Test book – you are now on your way to receiving your first horn certificate! Though the Prep Test is not an exam, you will be playing to an ABRSM examiner, who will write comments and suggestions on your certificate, ready to give you at the end. As you go through the Tunes, Pieces and Listening Games, your examiner will be listening out for two particular skills: playing the right notes and keeping well in time with a firm, steady pulse. These are both very important elements of music making, and will be the foundations of your future musical success.

The Prep Test is designed to be an enjoyable experience, and I hope you will feel pleased and proud to take your certificate away with you on the day. It will always be a reminder of your good work and achievement during this early stage of your musical learning journey.

I very much hope, too, that you will enjoy showing the examiner what you can do, and that your Prep Test will be the start of a long voyage of exciting musical discovery and fun.

Good luck!

John Holmes
Chief Examiner

AB 3843

1 TUNES

The examiner will want to hear you play all three of these tunes. You will need to play them from memory, so once you have learnt them remember to keep your book closed when you are practising!

a) Make It Long

Take a big breath and work on the dynamics. Are you making the fullest sound you can?

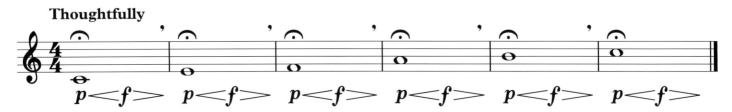

b) Make It Smooth

Try to move from one slurred note to another as smoothly as possible. Use lots of diaphragm support.

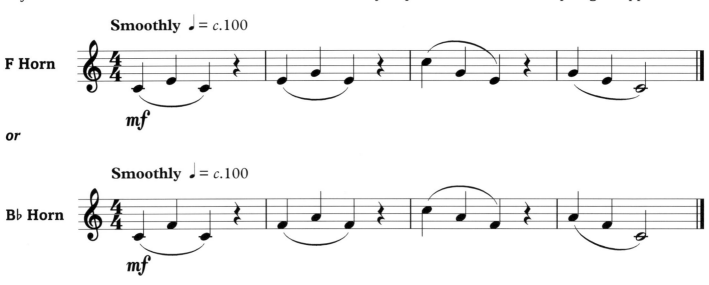

or

c) Make It Snappy

This piece is both jumpy and smooth! The notes with dots should be tongued and played short and light (this is called *staccato*). Make the slurred notes nice and smooth to create an effective contrast. Watch out for the accents!

2 FIRST PIECE – accompanied

Your first piece can be any one of the following three pieces printed in this book: 'Two by Two', 'Away in the Clouds' or 'Monkey Business'. Either the examiner or your accompanist will play it with you, so don't forget to bring the piano part.

Two by Two

Timothy Jackson

Away in the Clouds

Richard Bissill

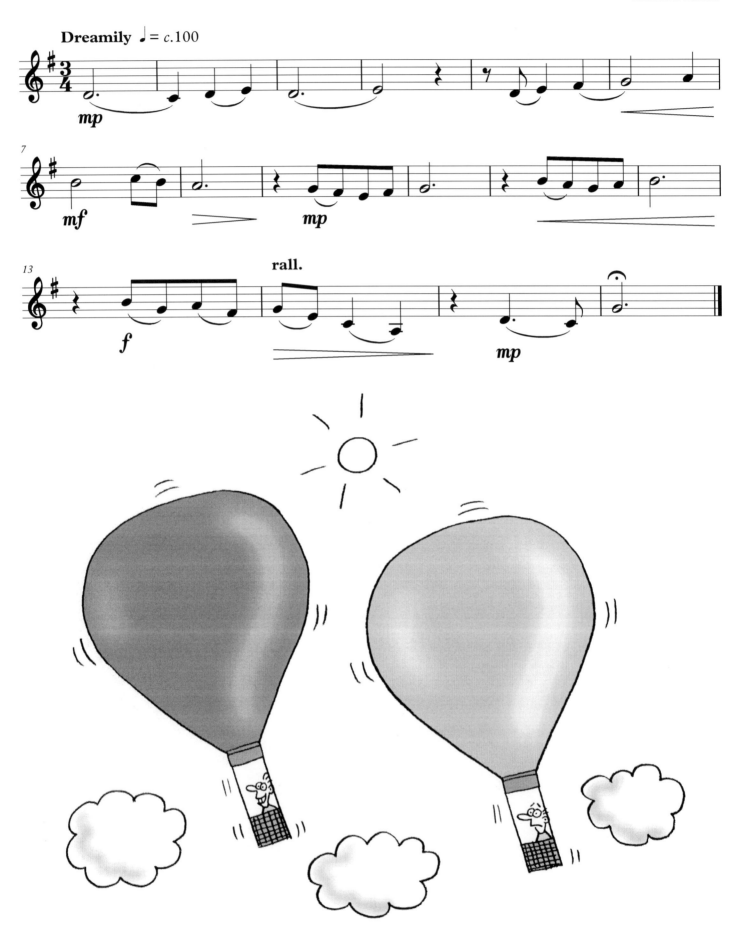

Monkey Business

Timothy Jackson

Away in the Clouds

Richard Bissill

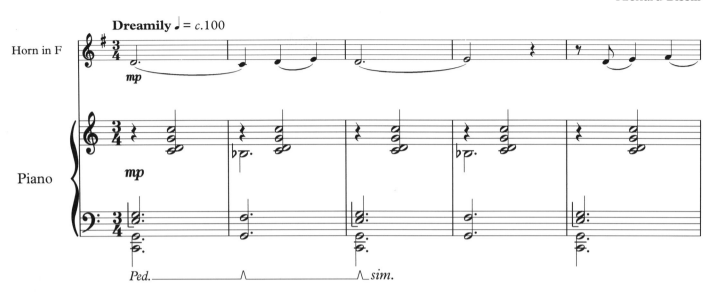

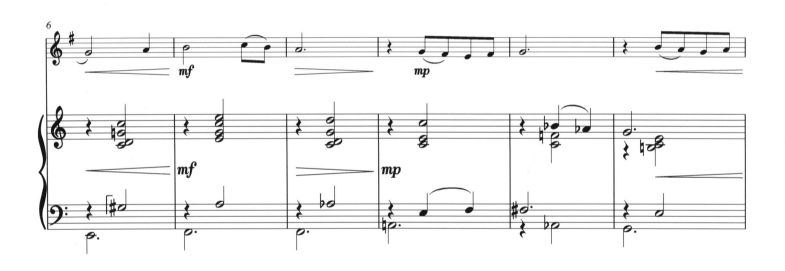

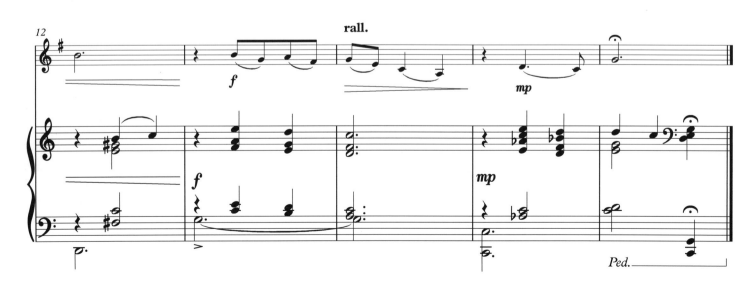

Two by Two

Timothy Jackson

Horn
Prep Test

Piano Accompaniments

AB 3843

Monkey Business

Timothy Jackson

3 SECOND PIECE – solo or accompanied

We would also like you to play a second piece. As we want you to play something you really enjoy, the choice is entirely up to you. If you choose to play an accompanied piece, don't forget to bring the piano part so that the examiner or the accompanist can play it with you.

4 LISTENING GAMES

In these four games the examiner will be playing pieces of music like the examples printed below.

a) Clapping the beat

In this first game, the examiner will play a short piece in 2 or 3 time. You should join in as soon as possible by clapping or tapping the beat.

This is a game you can practise easily by listening to music – all music has a beat. Why not try tapping the beat every time you hear some music?

b) Echoes

In this game, the examiner will clap two simple rhythms in 2 or 3 time. After each one, you should clap the rhythm back to the examiner in time, like an echo. The examiner will give a two-bar count-in.

You could practise this game with a friend or a parent. Did you clap *exactly* the same rhythm and keep the pulse steady?

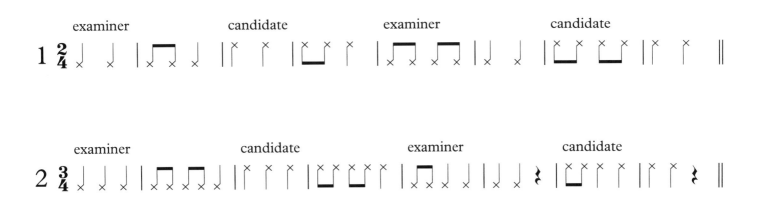

c) Finding the notes

Now the examiner will play a group of three notes to you, two times through. The game is to sing these notes back to the examiner after the second playing. If you don't want to sing, you can play the notes on your instrument – in this case, the examiner will play a group using only C, D and E. You have to find all three notes, including the starting note. Here are some examples:

Sing

or

Play

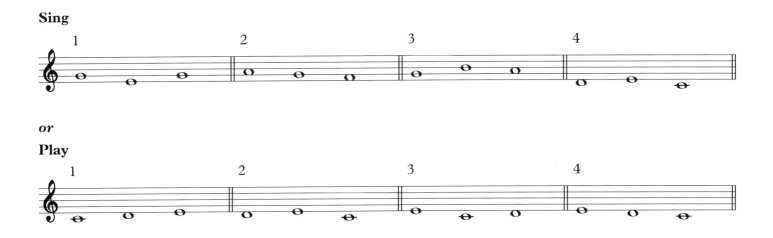

continued overleaf

d) What can you hear?

In this last game, listen as the examiner plays another short piece of music. The examiner will want to know whether the piece was played loudly or quietly (the 'dynamic' of the piece), or whether it was fast or slow (the 'tempo' of the piece). The examiner will tell you which one to listen out for before he or she plays.

You can practise this game with your friends whenever you are playing or listening to a piece of music.

i) Is this piece loud or quiet?

Robert Schumann

ii) Is this piece fast or slow?

Joseph Haydn

This crossword puzzle is just for fun. The answers to the clues are all musical terms and signs, many of which you will find in the music of your Prep Test book. Good luck!

ACROSS

3 The Italian term for quiet is ___ (5)

5 ◁— This means gradually getting ___ (6)

7 ○ This is a ___ (9)

8 > This is an ___ (6)

9 𝄴 means that there are four crotchet beats in a ___ (3)

10 The Italian term for loud is ___ (5)

12 𝄞 This is a ___ clef (6)

13 ♮ This is a ___ sign (7)

15 ♭ This is a ___ sign (4)

DOWN

1 ⌢ This sign means to ___ on the note (5)

2 ♪ This is a ___ (6)

4 —▷ This means gradually getting ___ (7)

6 ♯ This is a ___ sign (5)

7 ♩ The Italian term for the dot under this note is ___ (8)

9 𝄢 This is a ___ clef (4)

11 𝅗𝅥 This is a ___ (5)

14 𝄽 This is a crotchet ___ (4)

ANSWERS

ACROSS

3 piano
5 louder
7 semibreve
8 accent
9 bar
10 forte
12 treble
13 natural
15 flat

DOWN

1 pause
2 quaver
4 quieter
6 sharp
7 staccato
9 bass
11 minim
14 rest

Music and text origination by Julia Bovee
Illustrations by Alan Rowe (pp. 1 & 11) and Martin Shovel
Cover by Kate Benjamin and Andy Potts
Printed in England by Halstan & Co. Ltd, Amersham, Bucks.

06.16

AB 3843